Illustrated by Cindy Wilde
and Emily Golden Twomey

First published in Great Britain in 2022 by Buster Books,
an imprint of Michael O'Mara Books Limited, 9 Lion Yard,
Tremadoc Road, London SW4 7NQ

W www.mombooks.com/buster   **F** Buster Books   **T** @BusterBooks   **O** @buster_books

The material in this book previously appeared in *Amazing Copycat Colouring*,
Beautiful Copycat Colouring and *Brilliant Copycat Colouring*.

Copyright © Buster Books 2014, 2016, 2022

A CIP catalogue for this book is available from the British Library.

ISBN: 978-1-78055-832-5

2 4 6 8 10 9 7 5 3 1

This book was printed in May 2022 by
Shenzhen Wing King Tong Paper Products Co. Ltd.,
Shenzhen, Guangdong, China.

FSC
www.fsc.org

MIX
Paper from
responsible sources
FSC® C010256